Acknowledgements

Many thanks to Jackie Whi. helpful comments on an earlier draft of this story.

The author

Dr Susan Yarney is a Consultant Neurodevelopmental Paediatrician with a specialist interest in ADHD. She is the clinical lead for ADHD in her NHS organisation in Hertfordshire and is very passionate about creating awareness about ADHD and its impact on sufferers and families. She is the published author of a number of books that aim to promote an understanding of ADHD in children and young people affected with the condition.

The illustrator

Since graduating from Brighton Art College in 1996, Rachel Fuller has produced artwork for a range of magazines, design groups and advertising agencies. She is, however, predominantly known for her work in children's books. Rachel develops her own ideas, often in the form of novelty and interactive packages for young children. She also enjoys illustrating picture books, educational material and teen fiction. She has illustrated a number of books for BAAF, including *Morris and the bundle of worries*, *Elfa and the box of memories* and *A safe place for Rufus*.

The series editor

The editor of this series, Hedi Argent, is an established author/editor for BAAF. Her books cover a wide range of family placement topics; she has written several guides and a story book for young children.

Other books in this series

Oli and the pink bicycle – A story about a girl born with Foetal Alcohol Syndrome

Sam's trouble with words – A story about a boy with dyslexia

Why can't I be good? – A story about an adopted girl with behaviour problems

★

This is a story about a boy called Booh who has Attention Deficit Hyperactivity Disorder, or ADHD. If you find it difficult to stay still and pay attention, or if your behaviour gets you into trouble at home or at school – or perhaps you know someone who does – you may find Booh's story helpful. Even if you can read it yourself, you may want to ask a grown-up to read the story with you.

You may find that lots of the things that happen to Booh have happened, or are happening, to you. After you have read Booh's story you may have lots of questions about ADHD. There is a question and answer section at the back of this book with useful information about some of the things you may want to know about ADHD. Of course, if you have more questions you can ask the grown-up reading the book with you, your parent, carer, social worker or teacher.

★

My brother Booh has ADHD

A story about a boy with
Attention Deficit Hyperactivity Disorder

Susan Yarney

Illustrations by Rachel Fuller

Published by
British Association for Adoption & Fostering
(BAAF)
Saffron House
6–10 Kirby Street
London EC1N 8TS
www.baaf.org.uk

Charity registration 275689 (England and Wales)
and SC039337 (Scotland)

British Library Cataloguing in Publication Data
A catalogue record for this book is available from
the British Library

ISBN 978 1 910039 06 9

Project management by Michelle Bell, Publications
Department, BAAF
Designed and typeset by Fravashi Aga
Printed in Great Britain by the Lavenham Press
Trade distribution by Turnaround Publisher Services,
Unit 3, Olympia Trading Estate, Coburg Road, London
N22 6TZ

BAAF is the leading UK-wide membership organisation
for all those concerned with adoption, fostering and
child care issues.

To Amanda
(my late sister)

1

Dear Diary

I hope you don't mind if I give you a name?
I was very happy when I first saw you after
unwrapping layers and layers of paper. Mum
has this annoying habit of wrapping presents
up with lots of parcel paper. I bet she still
thinks we're little babies! You first came into
my life about six months ago, on my ninth
birthday. I've left you gathering dust on the
shelf in my bedroom since then. It's now time
to write about the thoughts in my head and
some important things happening at home
and school.

About your name – how do you like 'Panini'?

★

It's a silly name, I know, but paninis are my all-time favourite sandwiches, so I'll never forget your name. By the way, my nan makes awesome paninis.

I have to tell you more about my family and myself.

My name is Toby, very easy to remember. I have an identical twin brother called Booh. Being twins means that we were born to the same mum on the same day and identical means we look like each other so much that it is sometimes hard to tell us apart. People say that we look like two peas in a pod.

Booh and I were adopted when we were tiny babies. I have a little sister called Lisa who is also adopted. She is two-and-a-bit years old, and very cute. Being adopted means that our mum and dad are not our birth parents, but they love us just the same, and we're an ordinary happy family (well – most of the time). Dad is a postman and Mum stays at

★

home to look after my baby sister.

Booh is actually not my
brother's real name. His
proper name is Charlie. But
he hates the name Charlie
and will only answer to Booh.
I will tell you why he is called
Booh another day.

I need to be very careful about your hiding
place. I don't want my brother snooping
around my stuff and reading about the things
I write. I promise I will tell you about him
tomorrow. Booh can be very annoying indeed.
I sometimes wish I didn't have a brother at all.

I can hear my mum coming upstairs so need to
pretend I'm fast asleep. We'll talk another day,
good night!

★

Hi 'Panini'

It's a week since we talked and a lot has happened in that time. I did promise to tell you about my brother Booh.

I'm two minutes older than my brother. Mum said me and Booh were born a bit early and had to stay in hospital for a few weeks. When we were much younger, my brother and I were inseparable, which means we were very close. We look so alike, but we are very different in the way we behave. People say I'm the quieter and more sensible twin.

Booh gets into trouble all the time. This seems

★

to be getting worse as we grow older. People get surprised we're the same age because Booh acts more babyish.

You may be wondering how my brother got the name Booh. I can't remember the exact time but it may have been at the end of infant school. Booh liked to play silly tricks on the other kids by creeping up behind them and suddenly shouting 'BOO' in their ear, scaring them to death. He still does it to my little sister and me, and to children at school. Booh has been told off so many times by my parents and the teachers but he still goes on annoying everybody.

I think I hear my mum calling me to come down for supper. Let's chat later.

★

Hi!

School was good today. I did very well in my spelling test. I'm in the top sets for everything. My brother, on the other hand, is in middle sets for most subjects and even lower for English. He's really bad at reading. My mum says that Booh is very clever, which would show if he'd just stop playing silly tricks and jumping around. I do sometimes feel sorry for him, especially when he is told off all the time.

The other day, when Mum wasn't looking, he started flicking his pasta across the room, and then he tried blaming me for it! Can you believe this? I try not to argue with him;

★

I don't want to stress Mum out, but sometimes – no, most times – it's very hard to ignore my annoying brother.

I'm sure he loves our little sister, Lisa, but he can be a bit too rough with her. He looks very surprised and hurt when Lisa cries and won't play with him. I just try to keep out of his way! I think Booh is coming into my room – quick, let me hide you!

★

4

Panini

Wow, a really close call yesterday. No matter how many times I tell Booh to knock before coming into my room, he still barges in without asking. He ignores the 'PLEASE KNOCK BEFORE YOU ENTER MY ROOM' sign, just to annoy me!

Booh had to go to the head teacher's office again today. He got into an argument with a boy called Liam about something stupid. One thing led to another. Of course it was Booh who got the blame. Instead of explaining calmly to Mrs Walker, the playground assistant, he started crying and having his

★

usual tantrums. He ended up getting punished while the other boy got away with it. I know Liam and his friends did it on purpose so Booh would get upset and be angry. I hope they're ashamed of themselves now!

I do love my brother even though he annoys me most of the time. I feel sorry for him sometimes – no, most times. I'm feeling sleepy now. I'll tell you later why I feel sorry for Booh.

★

Hi there

I just came back from an awesome paintball
birthday party. It was great. There were about
15 of us. Booh wasn't invited to Billy's party.
He said he didn't care about not going to a
"silly" party. But I know he was upset because
I heard him crying in his room the day the
invitations were given out.

It's not the first time this has happened. I can't
even remember the last time Booh was invited
to a birthday party. I get invited to lots of
parties. And my friends are always coming to
my house and asking me back to theirs. Booh
does make friends, but he loses them quickly

★

because of his tempers and tantrums.

I hate it when teachers compare Booh and me.
'Why can't you be like your brother Toby?'
they ask.

Comparing us is a very bad idea. It just makes
Booh behave worse. Mum said she asked the
teachers to stop comparing us. But they still
do it.

I know I shouldn't be feeling guilty but I do.
I blame myself for Booh's naughty behaviour
sometimes. Maybe if I wasn't in the top sets
for everything, Booh would feel better. The
teachers should be telling Booh how good
he is at PE and football instead of
telling him off.

Booh is very good at football,
but he's already changed
football clubs three times.
He argues with the other
children, even at football

★

games. The last football coach told Dad that Booh loses his temper too much and doesn't listen to instructions. The coach in his new club is more patient with him. I hope Booh stays in this club.

I'm feeling sad about Booh at the moment and feel like reading something before bedtime to cheer me up a bit. Let's chat another time.

★

Hey Panini

I'm very excited. It's the three-day school trip to a place called Bower Water. There's going to be a lot of water activities. If the weather is good we might even sleep outdoors in tents. Me and my best mates are planning what games to take. We're all allowed to bring one each. Booh is very excited too. I hope he behaves himself and doesn't spoil the trip for everyone else. I feel sorry for Mum – she gets a bad report about Booh from school every day.
Dad says he doesn't know
how Booh is going to
cope in secondary
school.

★

I don't want to take you with me because my friends may think I'm not "cool" if they find out about you – no offence! I care what my friends think of me, not like Booh – he doesn't care or pretends he doesn't care. So chat when I'm back.

P.S. Don't miss me too much.

★

Hello Panini

I missed you a tiny bit. I had a wicked time! There was so much to do and eat! Kayaking, cycling, rollerblading, artificial rock climbing. We had a lot of barbeques because the weather was so good. We were even allowed to sleep outdoors in a large tent. Booh shared a tent with me and my friends because no one else wanted him in their tent. He had a good time too except for one awful thing.

Panini, Booh was given the fright of his life at the camp! A bunch of kids decided to teach him a lesson by playing a trick on him for a change. Ten boys were waiting for Booh when

★

he came out of the camp toilet in the dark. They all shouted a loud, long 'BOOOOO' together! Booh was so scared, he ran all over the place, screaming. He couldn't stop even when the boys were told off by the teachers and made to apologise. After that Booh begged me to go with him whenever he went to the loo. Maybe now Booh understands how people feel when someone creeps up behind them and shouts in their ear.

The teachers told Mum about it. I think she was very upset. Later, I overheard Mum talking to Nan on the phone about taking Booh to see a specialist to get him checked out in the school half-term holiday. It's very strange going to see a doctor for silly behaviour.

I think my baby sister wants me to get something for her. Talk to you later.

★

Hiya

We saw the paediatrician today. Mum said a paediatrician is a special doctor who takes care of children. I was very annoyed this morning when my parents told me I had to go with them to the hospital. Hospitals smell bad. I had to have some blood tests a few years ago at the hospital. I hated it.

Anyway the paediatrician's office wasn't like a hospital. She had loads of toys and books and nice pictures on the walls. I didn't see any needles – PHEW!

The doctor said Booh has something with a

★

long name called Attention Deficit Hyperactivity Disorder, but she said it was OK to call it ADHD. She explained that children with ADHD find it hard to keep still and do lessons because they can't concentrate, and they sometimes do silly things without thinking.

The paediatrician said Booh wasn't a "naughty" child, he just found it hard to stop himself doing silly things. She told us that important messages to help Booh think more about his behaviour and pay attention in class were not getting through to the right parts of his brain. Booh needs some special medicine and more help from everybody so these messages can get through and work.

But the paediatrician did tell Booh that having ADHD was not an excuse for being naughty.

I'm really glad I went to the doctor with Booh. I think I understand him better now. Maybe now things will work out for Booh at school and the football club.

★

Sorry Panini

I've been very busy with my school project – sorry I've not talked to you.

Good news – Booh is changing. He's really getting better! The special medicine's working. WOW!

A special nurse came to our school and talked to the teachers and class about ADHD. Booh said he didn't mind.

Booh and I don't argue so much now. My parents don't tell him off as much because Booh is listening to them more. I guess they're

★

more patient with him too. They've been going to some special classes to help them understand Booh better. And Jack invited him to his birthday party. Booh was so happy when he got his invitation.

Booh hates taking his medicine and is very noisy first thing in the morning. He wakes Lisa up every day. He can still be very annoying.

Booh says that he feels more confident since his visit to the paediatrician, especially as he's getting more help at school. He does some work with a special teacher and sometimes he sees the school nurse about his temper. He's learning how to stop and think before doing silly things that annoy the others. Booh told the nurse about the school camp, and how it scared him when all the children shouted 'boo' at him all at once. He promised he'd try not to shout at people and play silly jokes on them. I think Booh is happier now that he is not called naughty

★

by the teachers. I've also noticed that Liam and the other boys don't wind him up like they used to.

Panini, I really want you to know that I'm glad my twin brother, Charlie John Paul (J.P) Parker-Taylor, aka Booh, and me are getting on better – at last.

My favourite TV show is starting in three minutes – we'll talk more later.

P.S. 'aka' just means 'also known as'.

★

PLAY Booh's special Snakes and ladders game.

Now that you have finished Booh's story there may be lots of questions that you want to ask. If you have been reading this book with a grown-up, you could go through the questions that come next and talk about them together.

★

Is ADHD a word or short for something?

ADHD is an abbreviation or short for Attention Deficit Hyperactivity Disorder. Sometimes people call it ADD without the 'H', which stands for hyperactivity.

What is hyperactivity?

Hyperactivity makes it difficult to pay attention, to sit still for long or to think before acting.

★

Who gets ADHD?

ADHD is more common in boys than girls. The reason for this is not very clear. About five out of every 100 school children may have ADHD.

Can you work out how many children will have ADHD if you have 60 school children in a village? You can ask your mum or dad to help you.

If you have worked it out correctly, it means that three out of the 60 children will have ADHD. Hope you got that right. Can you imagine how many children will have ADHD if there are hundreds or thousands of children in a town or city? You can make up your own numbers and work out how many children will have ADHD.

How do you get ADHD? Can you "catch" ADHD like a cold?

Good question!

You can't catch ADHD like you catch a cold. Colds are mostly caused by viruses.

★

ADHD is not caused by a virus. In a lot of cases, it is not very clear what actually causes ADHD.

A lot of clever scientists have studied ADHD. These are some of the things scientists have written about why some people get ADHD:

1. Children who are born too early or are very small when they're born.

2. Children whose mums drank too much alcohol or smoked cigarettes when they were carrying a baby in their tummy.

3. Children who have parents, brothers and sisters or even grandparents with ADHD.

4. Children who get very ill with serious infections or are born ill.

Will I get ADHD if I eat too many sweets?

Eating too many sweets or sugar has not been shown by the scientists to cause ADHD.

★

Too many sweets, however, are not good for your teeth or your health.

Eating a good diet and making sure you exercise regularly is very healthy for your body and brain.

I'm scared of needles. Do you need a blood test to find out whether you have ADHD?

No. There are no blood tests or any other tests to show whether someone has ADHD or not.

How can I tell if someone in my class has ADHD?

You will know if someone has ADHD if they choose to tell you themselves. Generally, children with ADHD find it very hard to stay still, wait their turn or pay attention in class.

I will give you examples of what I mean:

Hard to stay still

Children with ADHD fidget a lot in class

★

during some lessons. They get out of their seat when they are not supposed to. They may interrupt lessons by calling out all the time. They like fiddling with their pens, paper and pencils in class. They sometimes make noises in lessons that disturb the other children.

In the playground, they can be very noisy and so full of energy that it's hard to keep up with them.

Younger children with ADHD like running and climbing all over the place. Their mums and dads have to keep a close eye on them so they don't hurt themselves.

Hard to wait their turn

Children with ADHD may butt into conversations and games without asking. They can blurt out wrong answers to questions in class because they weren't listening in the first place. Standing quietly in line for school dinners or class assemblies can be difficult for children with ADHD. Some of them do silly things

★

without thinking about the dangers –
like crossing a road without checking for
oncoming traffic. They may also lose their
temper very easily and act younger than
their age.

Not paying attention

Some children with ADHD are often referred
to as "being away with the fairies". This is
made worse when there is a lot of noise in a
room. When they are not paying attention,
they may lose bits of conversation which
can affect their schoolwork.

They may forget to tell their mum and dad
about birthday invitations and messages
from school. They may even forget to bring
their homework to school. They often lose
their books, toys and favourite things.

It looks like having ADHD is not easy.
Is it?

You are right.

Children with ADHD can be so overactive

★

in the day that they find it difficult to wind down and sleep at night. They wake up very tired and that makes it even harder for them to pay attention in class the next day. They make friends easily, but lose them very quickly. This can make them unhappy and sometimes lonely.

Doing dangerous and silly things like crossing roads without checking for oncoming traffic can lead to bad accidents. Not paying attention in class can affect their school work and lead to poor grades. This makes children with ADHD feel they are not good at anything even if they are very good at some things.

Can children with ADHD be helped at all?

Yes. There is a great deal of help for children with ADHD. Teachers who know a lot about it know exactly how to help children with ADHD to do better at school. They put them at the front of the class, and not near a window, to help them pay more attention. They may seat children

★

with ADHD next to pupils who pay good attention in class. These pupils are called "role models" because they show children who have difficulties how to do things well. Parents of children with ADHD can attend special classes and are given lots of information about ADHD so they can understand and help their children at home.

Do children with ADHD need medicine to get better?

Even though many children get better without medicine, some children with ADHD do need special medicine. Children who need medicine are seen often by a special doctor who knows a lot about ADHD.

Do they have to take medicine every day?

Most children with ADHD who need medicine will have to take it on most days unless told by their doctor not to.

All the pills need to be swallowed with a

★

glass of water; there are no liquid forms of the medicine. Some can be added to soft foods like yogurt if a child finds it hard to swallow pills.

How exactly does medicine help children with ADHD?

If children have ADHD, important messages to help them think about their behaviour do not quite get to special parts of their brain.

Think about the important work postmen do: postmen deliver mail to people's houses. If postmen in a town don't go to work for some reason, people may know they have mail in the post office but they wouldn't have any idea about what is in their letters or parcels. This means that the people in that town wouldn't be able to enjoy any exciting news or surprises in their letters and parcels.

Messages not getting through to special parts of the brain is just like postmen not being able to deliver letters or parcels. But

★

there may be hope for the town with no postmen. The post office may ask for help from another town's postmen so people can get their letters and parcels on time.

Just as postmen may need to come from another town to make sure parcels and letters are delivered, so for a child with ADHD, medicine, as well as assistance at school and from family and friends, will help to send important messages to special parts of the brain, when their own brain messengers or "postmen" cannot quite do the job on their own. These messages, once delivered to the special parts of the brain, will help children with ADHD to think more about their behaviour and how it sometimes makes other people unhappy. They will also be able to pay more attention in class and may even start doing well in their reading and other schoolwork.

How can I help someone who has ADHD?

You are already helping by asking the right questions and learning more about ADHD.

★

Children who have sisters and brothers with ADHD can sometimes go with them to see their doctors. This will help them understand their brother or sister better.

Please remember that children with ADHD can be a lot of fun!

And also remember to be patient with them as they are trying very hard to get better with the help they're getting from everyone, including, and especially, YOU!

★